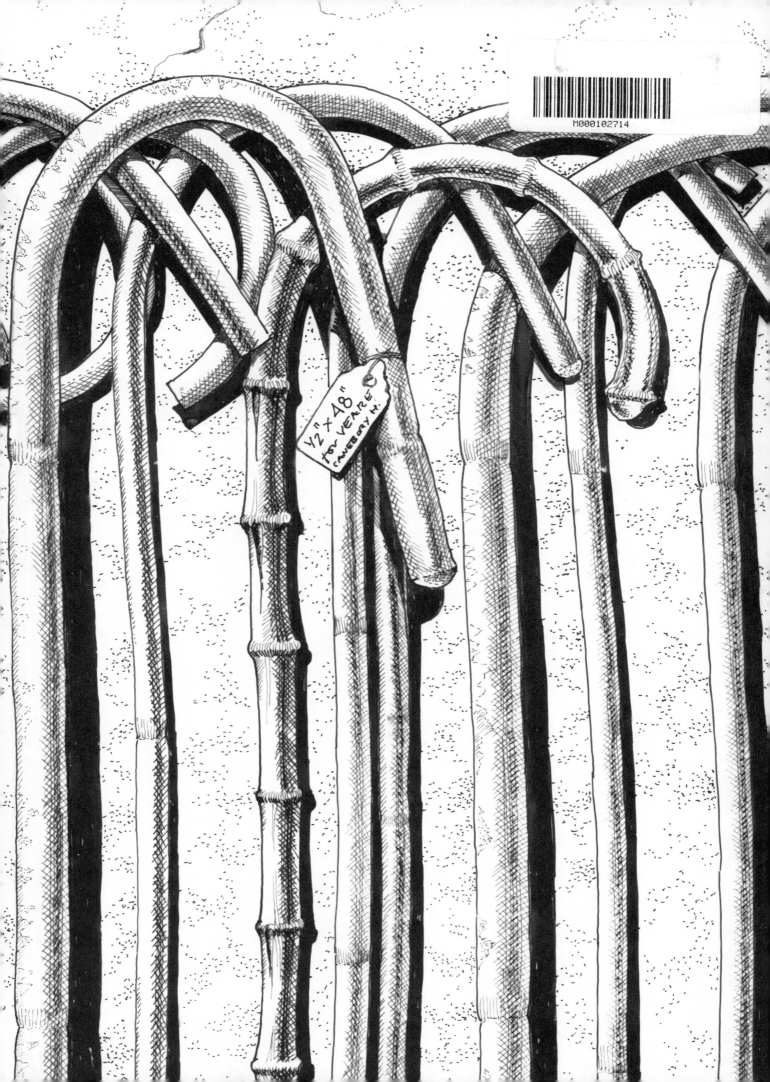

Frontispiece:

CLASSROOM DISCIPLINE.   The Duty Prefect lays on six of the very best for impudence and another twelve scorchers for breaking Rule 5. (P.15)

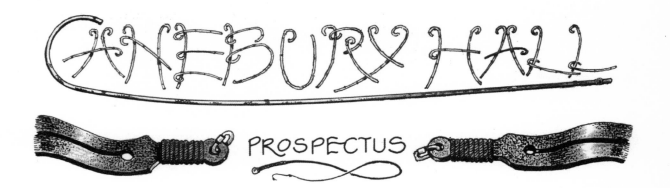

CANEBURY HALL

PROSPECTUS

Veronica C. Veare

Delineated By Greye

AKS
BOOKS
LIMITED

I

Published 2002 by
AKS BOOKS Ltd.
PO Box 39, Bexhill-on-Sea, East Sussex TN40 1WR England

Delineated by Greye

Also published by AKS Books:

THE ART OF DISCIPLINE
THE ART OF DISCIPLINE VOLUME TWO
A HISTORY OF THE ROD
THE WAND OF VENUS
EXPERIENCES OF FLAGELLATION
A PERFECT MISTRESS
ACROSS MY LADY'S KNEE
THE QUEEN OF THE GROVE
THE LOST BREECHES
CHÂTEAU SOUMISSION
FELLOWSHIP OF THE ROD I
FELLOWSHIP OF THE ROD II
MISS
OUCH!!
THE SONG OF THE CANE
THE KISS OF THE WHIP
THE WHIP AND THE ROD
TALES OF THE UNBREECHED
SWEET RETRIBUTION
LINTON ABBEY
TROUBLE AT LINTON ABBEY
IN FRONT OF THE GIRLS
THE SATURDAY AFTERNOON DETENTION
SENT FOR SIX OF THE BEST
THE SCHOOL RECORD
THE CANE THAT LOST ITS STING
and
THE GOVERNESS COMPENDIUM

A catalogue record for this book is available from the British Library.
ISBN 1899861 32 7

Designed in Great Britain.
Printed and bound by Antony Rowe Ltd.,
Chippenham, Wiltshire.

CONTENTS

The back stairs

IV

ntroduction

As Headmistress of Canebury Hall, I have been entrusted by the Board of Governors to administer their policies and curriculum. I am also responsible for the day to day running of our establishment.

This is a reformatory for miscreants of both sexes. Our purpose is to produce completely reformed and thoroughly trained pupils who will enter domestic service. We can accommodate up to twenty-two boarders, who are mostly orphans and foster offspring, placed here to be trained and disciplined as we deem appropriate. Six of the boarders are more advanced, "maids in training" who are here to improve their existing skills. They have a few privileges and less stringent rules, although the same standards of respect and obedience apply and violations are dealt with in Canebury style, the rod or leather.

We have a staff of very experienced teachers, along with six resident prefects, the Head Girl, a dedicated Matron and my personal maid. Other non-resident help includes two cooks, who work in shifts, a secretary and maintenance staff when required.

The following pages describe the workings of our school and we observe the tribulations of two pupils during their first day. We are very proud of our reputation for merciless corporal punishment. It is well founded and endorses the school motto,

"always on the bare!"

Veronica T. Veare. Headmistress

MORNING
Reporting

Entrance Hall

We start with the arrival of the new pupils, Miss J. Dobson and Master S. Bates. Dobson's foster parents have given up on her wild ways and decided that the setting of a strict reformatory will improve her attitude. A tall, very powerful girl for her age, she could be a useful servant with the correct schooling.

Bates comes from an orphanage. The instructions in his report read that, "This disgusting little runt must be whipped into shape!" He is 2 years younger than Dobson, almost cherubic in appearance, with one exception; a remarkably overdeveloped organ which seems to have a mind of its own. This has led him into much trouble, confusion and embarrassment and is the reason for him being sent here.

They have both been properly attired by the school clothier. Girl pupils wear a black knee length pleated skirt, a white cotton shirt, school tie, dark blue stockings (to mid thigh) with suspenders and black patent leather four inch heel strapped court shoes.

The boys wear a very high waisted white cotton shirt with frilled draw string, a deep Eton collar, short black jacket, open back draw string breeches, knee socks with garters and black buckle shoes.

The Headmistress reads their reports and inspects their appearance, making sure the underwear rule is complied with, and then places them in the appropriate class.

They will start in the Bottom Form taken by the terrifying Miss Phillips, described by Madame as, "My strictest teacher, in fact she gives a whole new meaning to the word!" Their first task will be to learn by heart, recited and written word perfect, the nine basic school Rules. When this is completed to teacher's satisfaction they begin normal morning curricula consisting of detailed lessons in servants' duties and etiquette.

Menial labours such as scrubbing floors, scullery work, general cleaning, polishing and so on are taught and applied in a practical way, ensuring that school premises are kept spotlessly clean and running efficiently.

Discipline is an intrinsic part of the Canebury Hall philosophy, so much so, that classes are offered on the subject to staff and prefects from other schools and teachers-in-training. In these classes Canebury pupils "in deep disgrace" are used for demonstration and practice.

"Headmistress' study"

Bates and Dobson waiting to report to Madame.

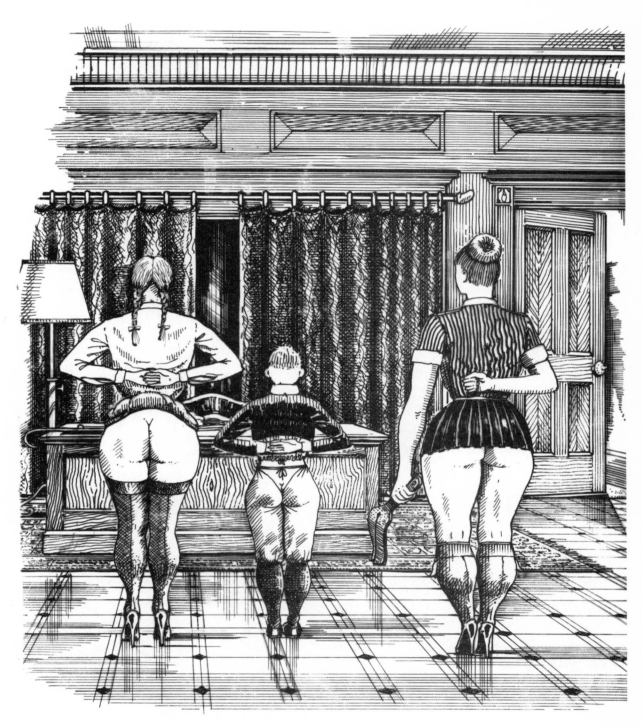

Behind the desk is a curtained one-way mirror
allowing visitors to view proceedings in privacy
and comfort.

Madame completes her inspection and the two
greenhorns are led off to class by Prefect Klyt.

The Bottom Form

Miss Phillips is indeed a fearsome woman! In her five inch heels she stands a towering six feet and eight inches. Broad shouldered and a strapping physique, she is well able to handle the most rebellious and dis-obedient pupils. A dedicated practitioner of the school's belief that the rod, leather and birch are the best teachers, these are a routine part of class.

She never hesitates to administer prolonged and agonizing punishment and inflict the cruellist humiliat-ion on both sexes. The flogging horse does not go unused for long.

We first see the classroom empty, prepared for eight pupils, four girls and four boys. Dobson and Bates will be made to kneel on teacher's rostrum steps while they learn the rules.

Echoing down the classroom corridor..... angry admonish-ment, the swish-crack of a brutal caning, the counting of strokes, the yelping of a hapless pupil..... ouch! ouch!

A duty prefect sits wat-chfully behind the pupils. Like all prefects she has 'at will' thrashing privileges using the leather tawse always carried. She also sometimes performs classroom caning and Assembly whipping duties.

11

The
duty prefect's
stool

The Bottom Form class starts at 8:00 am.

From left to right ; teacher's desk, chair, cupboard and stool, blackboard, dunce plinth, Rules scroll, disgrace bar and mirror, cane rack (including strap and birch), flogging horse and mirror.

13

RULES

1. To be learnt by heart and recited word perfect by every pupil. Any rule broken will result in an on-the-spot 12 stroke **THRASHING** with the cane or tawse from a <u>teacher</u> or <u>prefect</u>. Additional punishment may be prescribed at Detention or Assembly.

2. Correct forms of addressing superiors. Orders from the following must be obeyed <u>INSTANTLY</u>! Any hint of disrespect is considered a rule broken with the above consequences.

Headmistress	"Madame"
Teachers	"Mistress" "Master"
Matron	"Matron"
Prefects	"Prefect" "Head Prefect"
Others (maids, visitors, etc.)	"Miss" "Sir"

3. No pupil may speak unless addressed by a superior or first saying, "I beg for permission to speak please Mistress, Miss, etc."

4. Hands must be held behind back regulation style at all times unless ordered otherwise.

5. Regulation uniforms, detention and discipline tunics (which frequently replace pyjamas), to be worn neatly and correctly at all times. All underwear is STRICTLY forbidden! *

6. When addressed by a superior or upon hearing Madame present!", Mistress present!", etc, pupils must immediately stand to attention, hands behind back regulation style looking straight ahead.

7. Never sit without permission.

8. When pupils meet a superior outside class (corridor, stairs, etc.) they must face the nearest wall and adopt the position in Rule 6.

9. Dormitory etiquette as prescribed and strictly enforced by Matron must be followed to the letter! Included are the correct morning and evening procedures for rising and retiring, dressing and undressing, ablutions, inspections, serving and taking meals and studying at table.

BY ORDER OF V.C.VEARE, HEADMISTRESS

* Female pupils in heat are permitted to wear sanitary towels.

Even prefects are
not above a good hard rodding when necessary. This one
for lack of diligence. The two girls she is watching will
be reported later and "schooled" at evening Assembly.

16

The Bottom Form class in progress. Bates and Dobson kneel on the rostrum steps attempting to learn the Rules by heart.

The rest are proceeding with a lesson in dinner place setting and serving etiquette.

17

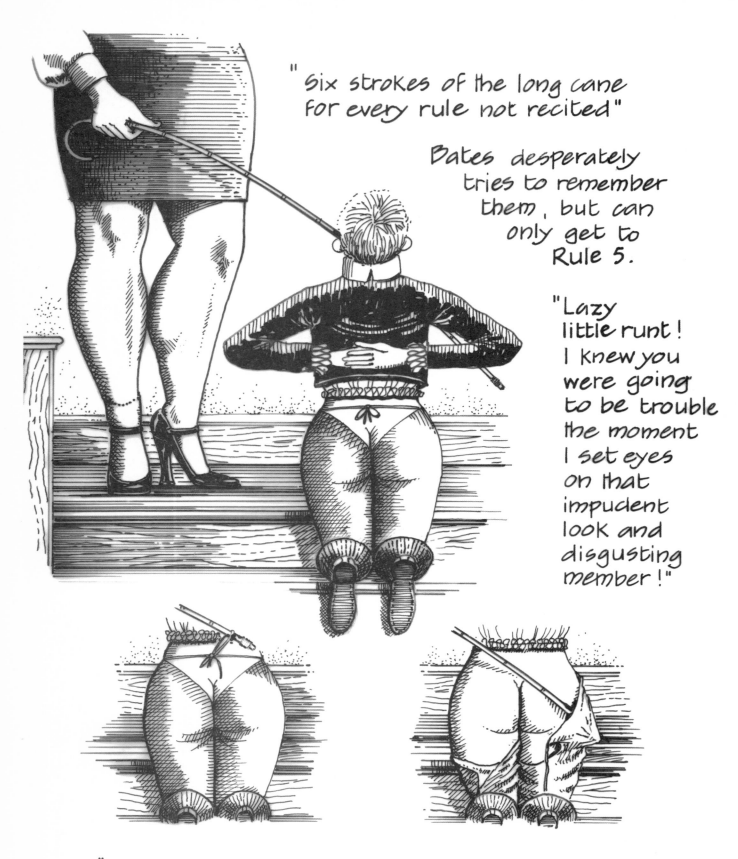

"Six strokes of the long cane for every rule not recited"

Bates desperately tries to remember them, but can only get to Rule 5.

"Lazy little runt! I knew you were going to be trouble the moment I set eyes on that impudent look and disgusting member!"

"Get over to the flogging horse......move it!"

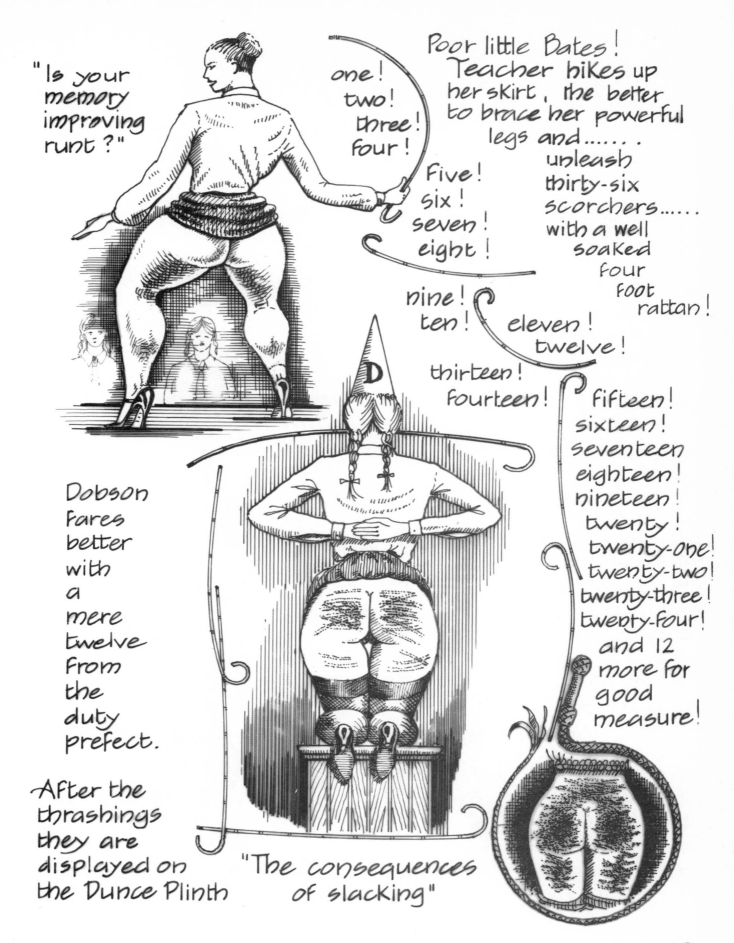

"Is your memory improving runt?"

one! two! three! four!

Poor little Bates! Teacher hikes up her skirt, the better to brace her powerful legs and.......

Five! six! seven! eight!

unleash thirty-six scorchers...... with a well soaked four foot rattan!

nine! ten! eleven! twelve!

thirteen! fourteen!

fifteen! sixteen! seventeen! eighteen! nineteen! twenty! twenty-one! twenty-two! twenty-three! twenty-four! and 12 more for good measure!

Dobson fares better with a mere twelve from the duty prefect.

After the thrashings they are displayed on the Dunce Plinth

"The consequences of slacking"

19

LUNCH TIME
Initiation

Hoping for some relief at lunch time, Dobson and Bates are horribly mistaken! Pupils take meals (usual fare being leftovers from superiors' dishes, supplemented if necessary with stale bread and water) at the refectory table in their Dormitory and serve each other by rota from the Kitchen on the floor below.

On their way upstairs our pair of innocents are waylaid by five prefects including the Head Girl, and bustled into their quarters. Compared to the Spartan conditions the pupils are made to suffer, these are quite luxurious with sprung beds, cotton sheets, extra pillows and blankets. But the lunch hour is about to become a cruel, painful and humiliating ritual.

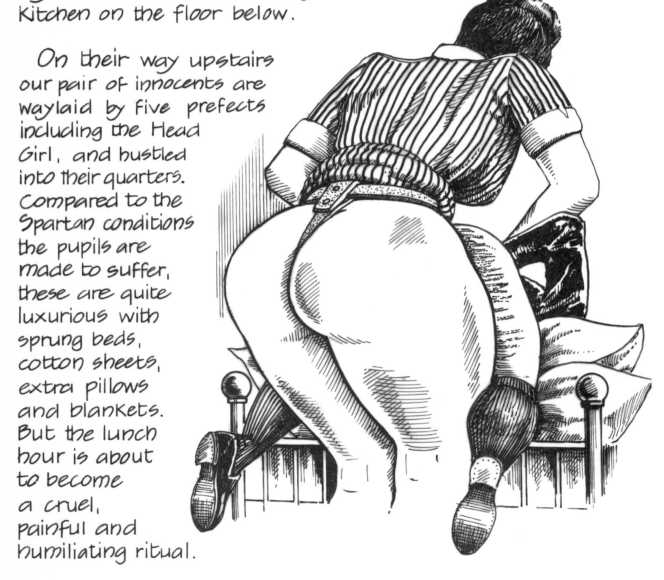

20

First the boy's breeches are ripped off. They tear quite easily being made of thin grey flannel. This leaves him naked from waist to knees. Dobson's skirt is removed with equal ferocity, torn completely down the side seam. Later, they will be punished by Matron for this 'shocking defilement' of their uniforms.

They are held face down over the feet of two beds and penetrated by each prefect in turn wearing a colossal strap-on. Five times the monster is thrust into Bates while the sadistic bitches pleasure themselves on it. Poor Dobson fares even worse as a double headed brute plunges into both orifices, and this is just the start.

The sickening ordeal continues in the adjoining bathroom. The wretches are forcibly held over lavatories, while the Head Girl relieves herself followed by the others. At the same time thighs and bottoms are belaboured with a rain of savage licks from the heavy leather tawse. Considerable masturbating takes place amongst the onlookers.

The weals from Miss Phillips' terrible classroom canings are still visible and are now overlaid with broad pink stripes from the leather.

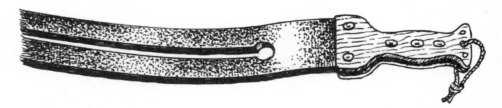

22

Both are dragged back to the prefects' dormitory where Bates is ordered to stand on a footstool, surrounded by the five bullies. Dobson is bent over, legs wide apart, high on tip-toes fully exposing her intimates to his view.

Since they started sharing their tribulations, the stripling of a lad has developed a fondness for this very mature, well-built girl. These feelings start to show in an exceedingly erect fashion, much to the hilarity of his tormentors, and the secret delight of Dobson, who starts to moisten uncontrollably.

They begin to to tease his ever growing totem with the tip of a cane. "I think this piglet is falling in love!" It stiffens, stiffens, stiffens and finally erupts, a sticky gush of ooze dribbling down the rod onto the prefect's crossed bare legs. He is ordered to, "lick up his mess!"

nosy maids get a lucky keyhole peep

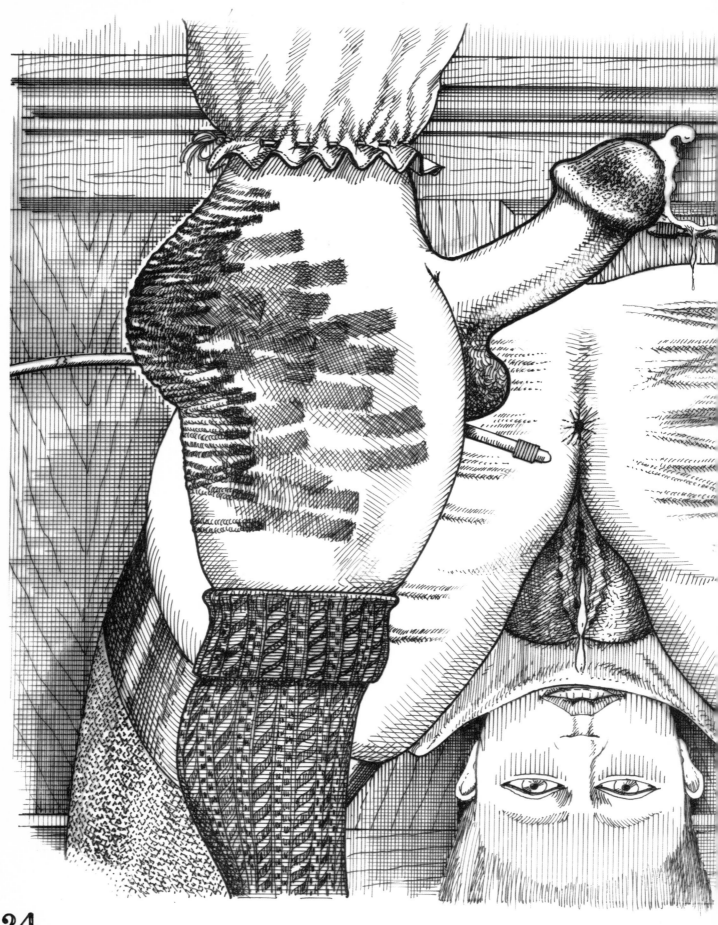

24

25

AFTERNOON
Staff Training Class

Lunch hour hell is over, but a new version is about to begin......

As luck would have it (actually by Madame's order) our reviled pair are chosen as the subjects of Staff Training Class. Teachers and prefects from other schools attend these popular classes to improve their discipline skills and learn new techniques. They are able to watch live demonstrations and participate in hands-on practice, much to their delight.

The curriculum covers most aspects of correction, from light to very severe. From verbal admonishment, shaming, humiliation and on to corporal punishment along with aftermath disgrace rituals. The instruments included are as follows :— The standard classroom canes (36 to 48 inches long), the leather tawse in various lengths and thicknesses, the birch, switch, horse bat and pig slapper. More advanced training introduces crops, dressage and cracking whips. Face and hand slapping are also taught.

After a fierce switching for 'answering back' to Teacher, a pupil is displayed on the Shame Pedestal in the Maids' Hall.

The class is usually taken by the Headmistress or her deputy. She delivers a verbal discourse and is ably assisted by an instructress who performs practical demonstrations. She is an extremely athletic young woman, a perfectionist who relishes her work. She has the assistance of two duty prefects.

Dobson and Bates are stripped and attired in punishment tunics, collars and micro-micro-micro-mini-minis.

Unknown to them, this is all they will be wearing for the rest of the

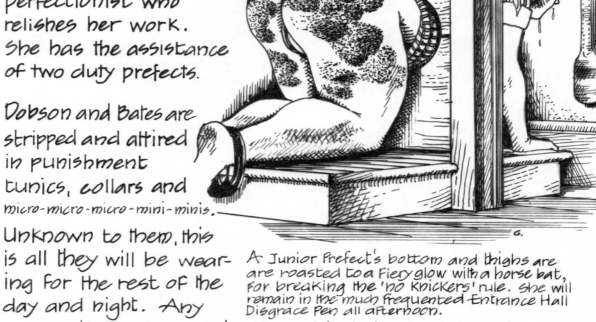

A Junior Prefect's bottom and thighs are roasted to a fiery glow with a horse bat, for breaking the 'no knickers' rule. She will remain in the much frequented Entrance Hall Disgrace Pen all afternoon.

day and night. Any areas left uncovered are subject to chastisement, the head being limited to face slapping, ear twisting and hair wrenching.

   Up to eight trainees can be accommodated. They sit on a dais along one wall until called upon to perform. The opposite wall is partly mirrored in front of which is a bar, sometimes serving as an alternative to the flogging horse. Madame sits at an elevated desk overlooking the room.

   Other items of note are the Shame Pedestal and Disgrace Pen. These are used to display harshly punished pupils as a warning to others, the Pedestal designed for extreme discomfort, the Pen less so, but very humiliating.

THE TRAINING ROOM

A dreadful sight for any miscreant who has the misfortune, like Dobson and Bates, to be relegated for demonstration and practice. The centrepiece is, of course, a flogging horse. To the left is

Madame's raised desk, flanked by cane and whip racks. Next, a Shame Pedestal, the trainees' dais, a squat lavatory and basin (for golden showers and brown bombings), and a Disgrace Pen. The floor is polished tile.

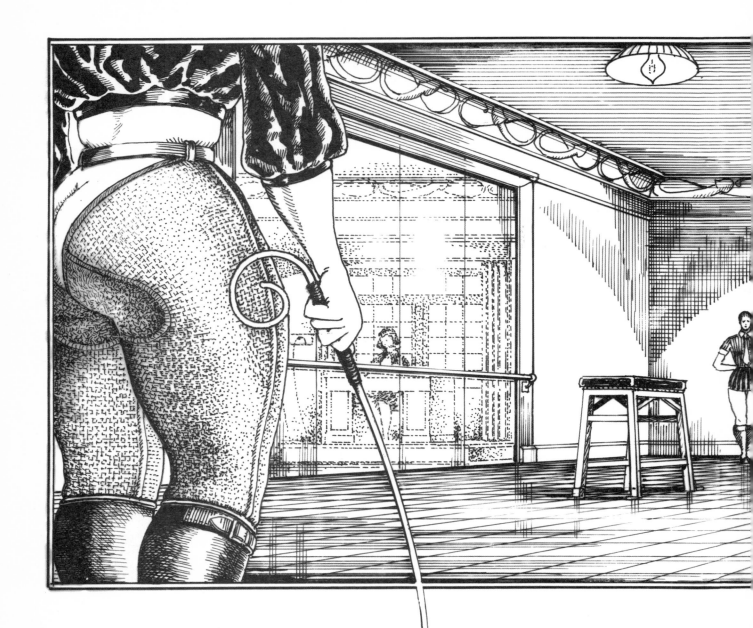

The two unfortunates are "run in" to the Training Room attached to six foot poles fastened to their disgrace collars. The poles will be removed before proceedings commence. To the left stands the instructress, sadistic and ruthless Miss Strictland, ready to start the **lesson in** basic caning techniques. Two prefects wait to assist as necessary, while eight trainees sit eagerly watching and waiting to learn.

We start with an exercise in respect. Dobson
and Bates are made to crawl on elbows and knees
to the dais, where they work down the line of young
women, licking their shoe soles and sucking the heels
in turn. The girls cross and re-cross their bare legs
for each shoe to be properly consummated to Miss
Strictland's satisfaction. She follows the pair with
wicked cane hovering over the upturned naked bottoms.

31

They crawl back to the flogging horse and discipline bar.

Madame opens with these comments. "There is no need to feel in any way sorry for these two miscreants. They are here for very good reason, having done things, if told, would make you blush to your toes. They will be trained properly and cured of their filthy, kinky ways! Therefore you should take every satisfaction in seeing them put to use for your education. They deserve every scorching stroke of the cane, every agonizing cut of the switch, every stinging lick of the strap! We will start with the standard classroom cane, beginning with the girl."

Miss Strictland steps forward. She first demonstrates, using Dobson as a model, the various discipline positions best adopted with the horse. Two of the most commonly used are ; hands on the top, legs spread wide apart on tiptoe, bare bottom pushed high·····or·····lying along the length face down, arms stretched forward legs together. Strenuous postures like these must be rigidly held throughout the punishment, or else !

And so begins three hours of purgatory for our pair of fledgelings. The lesson will finish at 5·00, but even then there will be little respite. They have to report for evening Detention at 5·15 as ordered by the still furious Miss Phillips.

THE MAIDS' HALL

Tea for two..... and for the girls' amusement, a Shame Pedestal in the corner. If occupied by a recently thrashed miscreant, these two very attractive and sensual young lassies might not be so engrossed with each other.

Maids are encouraged to torment, tease and inflict additional punishment with the instruments provided on any pupil, of either sex, 'sitting' on this cruel and humiliating device.

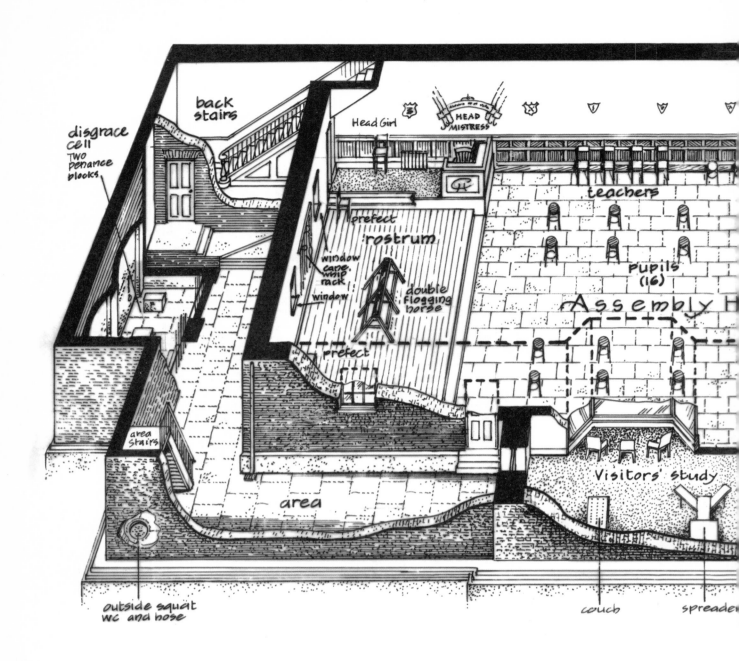

Labels on illustration:

back stairs

disgrace cell
TWO penance blocks

Head Girl

HEAD MISTRESS

teachers

prefect

rostrum

window cane whip rack

window

double flogging horse

pupils (16)

Assembly H

prefect

area stairs

area

Visitors' study

outside squat WC and hose

couch

spreader

THE BASEMENT

The primary space is a handsome Assembly Hall, which features seating areas for teachers, prefects, maids, and pupils. The Headmistress' dais overlooks the entire hall, including punishment rostrum one end and at the other, obedience training circle and detention desk.

From top left to right, we see Madame's private back stairs to her flat and upstairs corridors, the

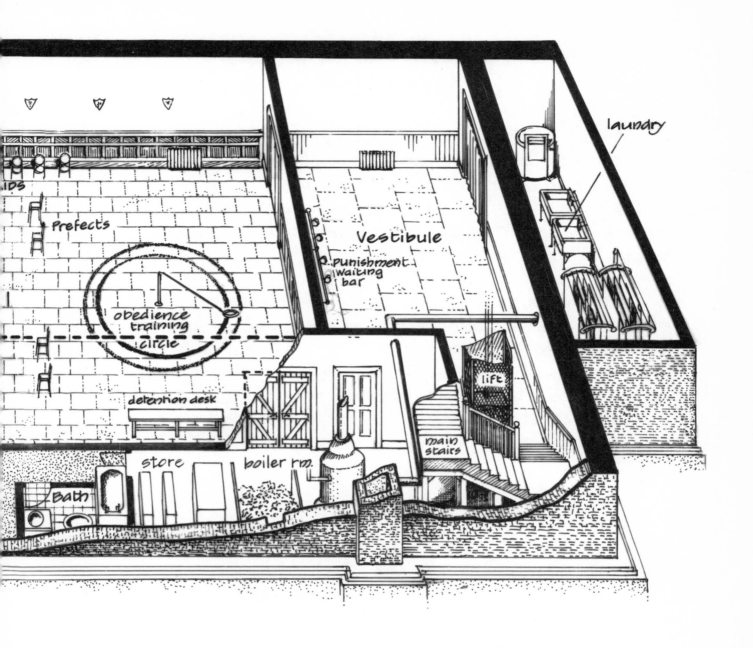

laundry

Vestibule

Prefects

obedience
training
circle

punishment
waiting
bar

detention desk

store   boiler rm.

Bath

lift

main
stairs

outside disgrace cell, area and stairs to back door.
Then, a small study for visitors and others to view
proceedings and indulge themselves with selected
pupils as their lust dictates. A bathroom adjoins.

A store and boiler room, vestibule (with kneeling bar for
miscreants waiting to be 'schooled'), main staircase,
lift and laundry room complete the layout.

EVENING
Detention

Escorted by the grim faced Prefect Strapworthy
Dobson and Bates arrive at the detention area
at the rear of the Assembly Hall and, on their
knees, wait for the appearance of Miss Phillips.
Evening detention usually lasts from 5:30 to 8:00 pm
before evening Assembly.

Still seething at what she calls, "inexcusable
slacking and impudence" in class, she gives them
the impossible task of writing out the Rules fifty
times in twenty minutes, word perfect. She threatens
an obedience training session if they fail to comply.
Mistress and prefect leave the room and for
the first time our poppets are alone together.

Cheeks still marked and quivering from Bottom
Form canings and Staff Training Class, Dobson and
Bates kneel at the detention desk waiting for
Mistress. Bates embarrasses himself again.

They kneel side by side, writing out their lines in careful neat script. A whispered conversation starts with Bates apologizing for his crude reaction to her body at the 'initiation'. "I felt so embarrassed, but just could not control myself" he stammers. "Don't worry" she breathes, "Actually if all that was for me, I was quite flattered." With these words the same thing starts to happen. They both look at it and blush furiously. She starts to gently finger herself and begins to moisten, at the same time reaching out with her left hand to fondle the huge purple helmet.

They hear the click, click, click of approaching heels, prefect is returning. It is immediately obvious to her what has been happening, so she about turns to fetch Miss Phillips, "This time they need a real lesson!"

In a few minutes the more purposeful and angry click-clickity-clickity-click of two pairs of high heels echo down the stairs and vestibule. The door is flung open, Mistress pauses shaking with rage, and then strides over to the desk. "You first, dirty, dirty, dirty little runt!" She grabs Bates by his ear and drags him over to the Training Circle, attaching his collar to the pole.

"Run, filth, run, move it!" Mistress and prefect stand on opposite sides of the circle, Pig Slappers at the ready. As he passes them in turn, they deliver a barrage of stinging licks. "Halt runt!" snaps Mistress, after twelve laps, "Now let us begin the real lesson!"

38

39

This is the start of a prolonged and elaborate lesson in dressage steps which include, slow high-stepping, fast and slow trotting, cantering and so on, the purpose of which is to instill complete subservience and instant response to orders. Commands are given with a variety of crops and cracking whips.

The lesson seems to go on forever........

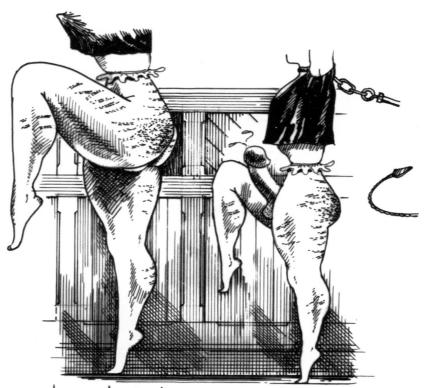

up! up! up!   crack-crack-crack!!!

Exhausted and covered with welts they are finally returned to the detention desk and continue with writing their lines until the start of evening Assembly.

⌒ Assembly ⌒

The entire school troops into Hall. Teachers, prefects, Matron, maids-in-training, pupils, and finally the ruthless and unforgiving Headmistress.

Teacher

The gathering falls to its knees. Madame recites Evening Prayers after which all rise to mount their respective stools.

Matron

The main event tonight is the 'schooling' of two mis-creant girls. Their offences are the breaking of Rules 3 and 4, and mutual self-abuse in class (see P.17). The Headmistress prescribes the length and severity of punishment, in this case 24 lashes of the dressage whip. Being a 'double schooling', each girl receives alternate strokes.

Prefect

When this brutal and prolonged ordeal is concluded and the weeping, squirming young offenders are returned to their stools, (which they can hardly bear to sit on), Dobson and Bates are hauled up to the front and given close-crop 'disgrace haircuts'.

Maid

41

A Peeping Tom's view from the Area. The coveted duty of wielding the whips goes to a pair of bully-

bitch dykes, Prefects Strapworthy and Rampling-Styng.
After Assembly pupils are led off to their dormitory.

The school's most dreaded
flogging horse.........

" STRAP THE FILTH DOWN ! "

NIGHT
Dormitory

The pupils' dormitory has a multi-purpose. Not only do our miscreants sleep here, they take their meals at the refectory table, where morning and evening prep is also performed.

The beds are arranged in rows of four with a total of sixteen (this can vary). They are wood framed and bedding consists of a thin horsehair mattress on boards, a similar pillow and hessian blanket. When necessary pupils can be secured to their beds with a lockable slip chain collar.

Dormitory is effectively run by Matron, a woman who has absolutely no tolerance for the slightest infraction of the Rules and her own procedures. Rising and retiring routines are closely monitored with dire consequences for any hint of misbehaviour. Dressing and undressing takes place at the lockers in the adjacent corridor, while ablutions are carried out in the bathroom at one end, where showers and squat w.c's are located.

Two prefects are always on duty during dorm hours and have their own sleeping, sitting and dressing quarters which overlook the whole room.

A general view
of the pupils' dormitory,
showing the arrangement of
beds, prefects' overlook stations,
refectory-prep table and of course the much
used and brutally uncomfortable flogging horse.

46

47

The fondness that Bates has for Dobson now develops into full-blown, uncontrollable lust. So, after lights off, in spite of knowing very well the consequences if caught, he crawls silently over to her bed.

She has been praying that this would happen and eagerly presents herself for him to start feasting.

So engrossed in this delicious bliss, they are oblivious to the two prefects, watching and waiting for the right moment to interupt the rapidly climaxing boy and girl. The lights snap on! Matron is called...

48

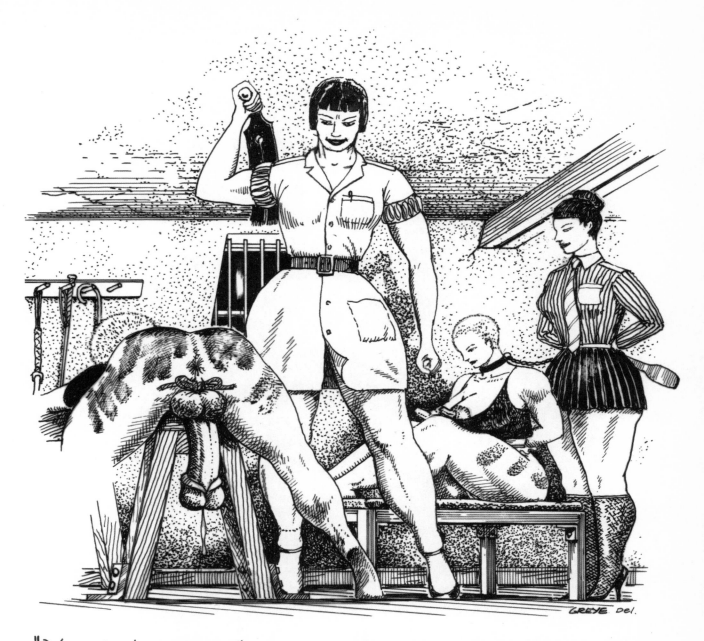

"You don't know what a real thrashing is until you've had one from me, you filthy little piece of pig shit!"

Matron's leatherings are so ferocious that miscreants have to be tightly secured to the flogging horse with a thick waist strap and cords. Dobson and Bates will both suffer 48 savage licks of the heavy tawse and then spend the night in the outside cell chained to penance blocks. In the morning they will be severely 'schooled' at Assembly.

49

With the windows open
   On this Summer night,
      The sounds of leather "on the bare"
      Float down to the street,
         Matron's wrath!
      The counting of strokes!
         Miscreants' cries!
            The thwacking
            of a heavy strap
               on shuddering
                  cheeks...

Thus ends the First day for our two pupils.
Perhaps a little harsher than a typical one,
but well illustrates the school's commitment
to produce well trained, dutiful and
obedient servants.

50

Floor plans

The next two pages show floor plans from Basement to Fourth Floor. Studying these will clarify the layout of facilities offered at Canebury.

Basement. Assembly hall and vestibule, outside area and cell, visitors' study with bathroom, store, boiler, laundry.

Ground Floor. Entrance hall, Headmistress' Flat, study & office/library.

First Floor. Classrooms, Guest rm/store, WC.

Second Floor. Training room, Matron's Flat, Common rooms

Third Floor. Refectory for teachers, prefects and maids, Kitchen, dormitory (prefects' and maids') bathroom.

Fourth Floor Pupils' dormitory and bathroom.

Abbreviations and symbols.

bl	blackboard
cr	cane rack
cws	cane, whip & strap rack
cn	curtain
c	cupboard
db	discipline bar
dc	disgrace cage
dp	disgrace pen
dpl	dunce plinth
fh	flogging horse
h	hose
hg	head girl
hm	headmistress
kb	kneeling bar
L	lift
M	mirror
owm	one way mirror
pb	penance block
pr	prefect
rt	refectory table
sp	shame pedestal
+ +	showers
sc	study couch
s	spreader
o	squat wc
◁	squat bidet
t	teacher
wp	whip rack

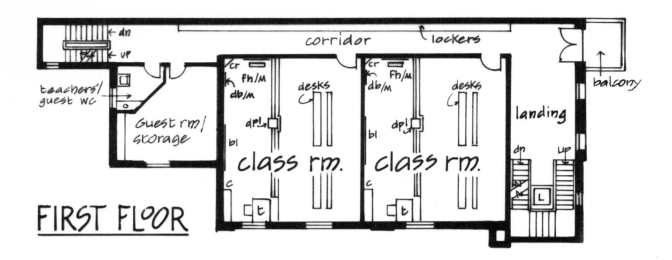

FIRST FLOOR

- dn
- up
- corridor
- lockers
- balcony
- teachers'/guest wc
- Guest rm/storage
- cr
- fh/M
- db/M
- desks
- cr
- fh/M
- db/M
- desks
- landing
- dp!
- bl
- class rm.
- dp!
- bl
- class rm.
- dp
- up
- c
- t
- c
- t
- L

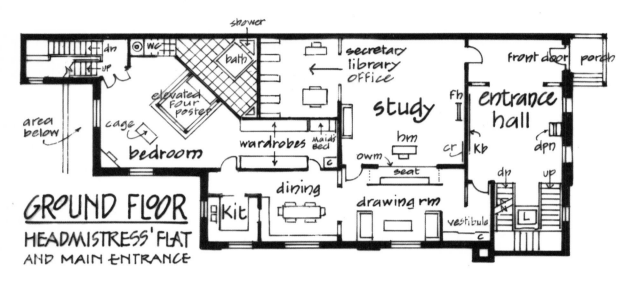

GROUND FLOOR
HEADMISTRESS' FLAT
AND MAIN ENTRANCE

- dn
- up
- wc
- shower
- bath
- secretary library office
- front door
- porch
- elevated four poster
- study
- fh
- entrance hall
- area below
- cage
- bedroom
- wardrobes
- Maids Bed
- c
- owm
- hm
- cr
- Kb
- dpn
- dp
- up
- dining
- seat
- drawing rm
- vestibule
- kit
- c
- L

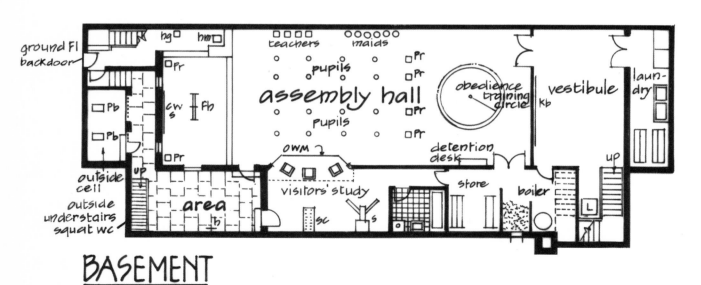

BASEMENT

- ground Fl backdoor
- hg
- hm
- teachers
- maids
- Pr
- Pr
- pupils
- Pr
- obedience training circle
- vestibule
- laun-dry
- Pr
- assembly hall
- Pr
- Pb
- cw s
- Fb
- pupils
- Pr
- detention desk
- Pb
- Pr
- owm
- store
- up
- outside cell
- UP
- area
- h
- visitors' study
- sc
- s
- boiler
- L
- outside understairs squat wc

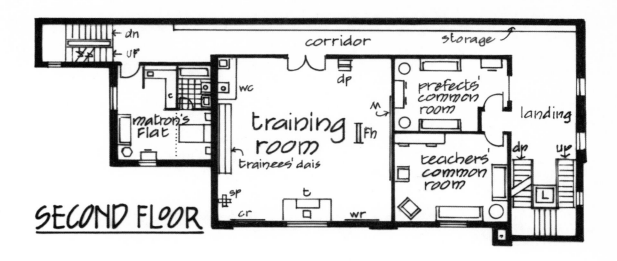

SECOND FLOOR

dn

UP

corridor

storage

wc

dp

matron's Flat

c

training room

M

Fh

prefects' common room

landing

teachers' common room

dp

up

L

trainees' dais

sp

t

cr

wr

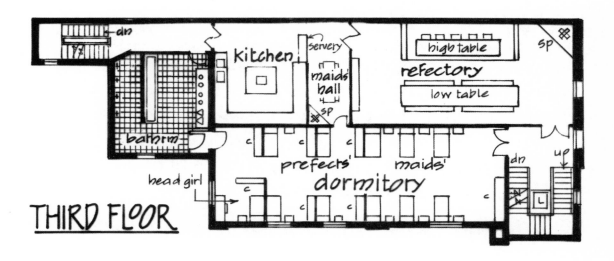

THIRD FLOOR

dn

kitchen

servery

high table

sp

maids' hall

refectory

sp

low table

bathrm

c

c

c

c

head girl

prefects'

maids'

dn

up

c

dormitory

c

c

c

L

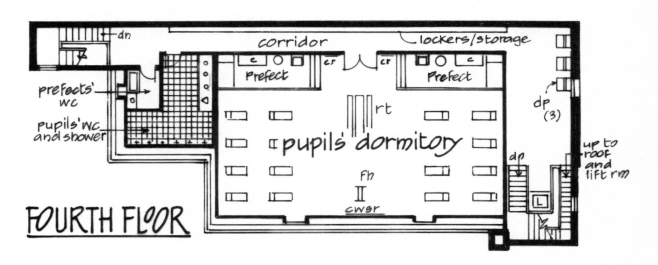

FOURTH FLOOR

dn

corridor

lockers/storage

c

cr

cr

Prefect

Prefect

prefects' wc

dp (3)

pupils' wc and shower

rt

pupils' dormitory

up to roof and lift rm

Fh

dp

cwgr

L

53

POSTSCRIPT

Three weeks have passed. Dobson and Bates are now sufficiently well trained to serve as "toys" to a Mistress or Master.

Their first outing is to the annual Dykes Ball, under the supervision of Miss Phillips herself, resplendent in evening finery. Her bold formal gown is exquisitely crafted in the sheerest latex, the chainwork and thigh band of steel. (her favourite dance is a slow Tits to Tits, but she is also a very hot Foxtrotter!)

As a feature of the night's entertainment we see Master Bates being put through his paces, while Dobson waits in the wings for her cue to join this performance of Hold-The-Feather (or else!).

The gathering of young lesbians is greatly amused, and aroused. The hours of ruthless training are proving their worth.

FINIS

55

CHÂTEAU SOUMISSION

Château Soumission is the stunning second book from the author of *The Queen of the Grove*; it includes two full-length novellas. *Château Soumission* is the ultimate "closed world", where Ladies rule, Domestics serve and the Rod is paramount… The second story is *Miss Beauchamp's Reward:* "For years she had served Our Lady of the Rod faithfully and in her own way—without once taking an active rôle. But now her time had come…"

£20.00

THE LOST BREECHES

When Pepin leaves home to seek his fortune things go badly wrong almost immediately. Within a few hours he has received the spanking of his life from an angry innkeeper's wife—and has lost his breeches into the bargain. His sole wish thereafter is to retrieve them. *The Lost Breeches* follows his unhappy odyssey as he pursues the missing garment—a journey all too frequently interspersed with the use of the Rod upon Pepin's person by the lady he has most recently annoyed: and there is no shortage of these. A delightful fairy tale illustrated by Curtus with 33 original plates.

£25.00

ACROSS MY LADY'S KNEE

When three teenage daughters of the 21st-century *belle-monde* each decide to acquire a pageboy as the latest fashion accessory, life changes drastically for the youths most closely concerned. Well-fed, well-housed and (particularly) well-dressed, the three pageboys are nevertheless also extremely well-disciplined, subject to frequent and humiliating corporal punishment at their young mistresses' whims. What follows over the next eighteen months is a prolonged—and profound—learning experience for all concerned. With 13 original plates by Curtus.

£25.00

A PERFECT MISTRESS

Jacqueline Ophir's latest full-length novel, partly a work of imagination and part autobiographical, tells the story of Miss Leah B—, who, while still in her early twenties, is obliged—by Fate, as it seems—to confront the reality of her inclinations when she disciplines a rowdy youth in the street. Soon afterwards she receives a letter from a distraught mother, asking for help of a similar nature—and so begins an extraordinary career as *A Perfect Mistress*. An exquisitely written work by the Editress of *The Governess* journal, gorgeously illustrated throughout by Sardax with several full-size watercolour plates and a large number of sensitive motifs.

£25.00

LINTON ABBEY

WHEN WILLIAM was sent to join his cousin Lucy at her mixed boarding school, he had no idea what was in store for him.

What was in store for him was the same thing Linton Abbey School provided in full measure for all its boy (but never girl) pupils.

The Hairbrush. The Slipper. And the Cane.

Always on the bare bottom, and nearly always in front of the girls. Then William and his friends rebelled…With six original plates by Curtus.

£15.00

TROUBLE AT LINTON ABBEY

SCHOLASTIC DISCIPLINE of an unusual kind! When Americans, Laura and Howard won a scholarship to Linton Abbey School, in faraway England, they had no idea what they were in for. Particularly Howard. For Linton Abbey was the kind of school where corporal punishment was the everyday answer to boys' youthful peccadilloes. Always administered on the bare bottom, and nearly always in front of the girls! Then Howard and his friends hatched a plot…

£15.00

IN FRONT OF THE GIRLS

THIS ENGAGING and provocative collection, by the author of *Linton Abbey*, is devoted to exploring the proposition that for a male to be punished in the presence of—or by—the opposite sex of the same age is perhaps the ultimate mortification. Short stories and poems of rare quality and vivid imagination, illustrated throughout with full-page plates by Sardax, make *In Front of the Girls* Miss Blackwood's most exciting and accomplished work to date.

£15.00

SWEET RETRIBUTION

A CHARMING COLLECTION of essays and poems, originally intended for *The Governess*, but never published in that Journal for reasons of apace alone.

This constantly popular selection includes: *The Nun's Story*; a terrifyingly true tale of how the sisters in a Breton convent punished the girls; *Community Care*; in the not too distant future, women rule Society and the Rod is back—with a vengeance! *Singapore Sting*; a young teenager steals a brass plaque, but is found out—for an English girl the punishment is extremely severe!

£10.00

THE KISS OF THE WHIP

THIS comprehensive and fully illustrated study of corporal punishment was first published in 1961 when, 13 years after its abolition, there was a public clamour to restore flogging to the penal code.

Chapters cover religious flagellation; superstition and persecution; wife-beating and parental punishments; 'educational' flogging in fact and fiction; flogging in the armed forces; judicial flogging; flagellation in brothels; the whipping of male and female servants; sadism and masochism; and the physical, sexual, and psychological effects of whipping.

£15.00

TALES OF THE UNBREECHED

'TAKE DOWN your trousers…' is the most deadly and intimidating command that may be uttered in a disciplinary environment. *Tales of the Unbreeched* covers hundreds of ways of endowing this seminal disciplinary task with flair, imagination and effectiveness, illustrated with sumptuous original artwork by Curtus as well as dozens of other cogent images. Edited by Jacqueline Ophir

£15.00

MISS

MISS tells the story of a young lady of quality, sent by her stepmother to a strict boarding school in Flanders, which is run by a passionate female flagellant. Lucette relates her recollections of boarding school discipline, and the intimate details of her own chastisement under the strict régime.

On leaving the school, she returns home to find that the same disciplinary methods await her at the hand of her stepmother.

After her marriage and the untimely death of her husband, she agrees to take care of her young niece, who experiences the same punitive environment, along with one of the maids.

£25.00

THE WAND OF VENUS
The High History of the Birch Rod

A DAZZLING and erudite compendium of birchen lore, compiled from a huge variety of expert sources from classical times to the present day.

It includes histories, anecdotes, eulogies, factual accounts, recommended procedures and other Arcana of the Rod, intriguingly assembled and beautifully presented with over 80 rare and original illustrations.

£25.00

THE SATURDAY AFTERNOON DETENTION

'FOR ONCE, I was disappointed not to see a cane lying on her desk, as it would've meant that Lucinda was wrong about our crimes being reported for Mrs. Vincent's rigorous attention. After the Headmistress, it was Miss Cartwright's cane that all the girls feared most, but even an immediate thrashing from her would be preferable to the Saturday detention that was now on the cards.'

Angela Richards recollects her very personal experiences of attending a Girls' Boarding School in the early 1960s, sensitively describing her fears and the painful events which unfold on the day that she and her two best friends had to report to the Headmistress's study for a *Saturday Afternoon Detention*.

£15.00

SENT FOR SIX OF THE BEST

IN this sequel to *The Saturday Afternoon Detention*, Angela has been caught smoking in the Fourth Form washroom by bossy-boots prefect, Amanda Wilkinson. Last term, the Headmistress had decreed that if Angela, Nicola or Caroline were caught smoking again they were to be sent to either her, or Miss Cartwright for six of the best! Angela pleaded with Amanda to take her to the Duty Mistress to be punished, as she knew that if she escorted her to Miss Mitchell, her Form Mistress, she was sure to refer her to Crusty Cartwright, the irascible Deputy Headmistress for six of the best!

£15.00

THE SCHOOL RECORD

"BEND OVER your chair," she instructed.

Remembering how Madame always seemed able to make it sting more than most of the other mistresses, even though she never raised the cane any higher, I did as directed. With my back to the rest of the class and gripping the flat, latticed seat in readiness, I looked down knowing it'd be virtually impossible to sit there through the rest of the lesson...'

Set in a strict Girls' Boarding School during the mid-1960s, you can almost hear the sound of chalk squeaking against the blackboard and the swish of the mistresses' canes! Now in the Fifth Form and just sixteen, Angela and her friends giggle and painfully wriggle through the last week of term before the Easter hols. Caroline first mentioned it at lunchtime as a joke, but Barbara Nicholls decided to ask Miss Robertson whether it had ever happened before. Angela is faced with a terrible dilemma... should she attempt the 'School Record'?

£15.00

THE CANE THAT
LOST ITS STING

"BUT HOW can I tell whether or not it has lost its sting?" Mrs. Bonnington questioned.

"Lost its sting?" Nicola repeated, incredulously.

"Sting!" she replied. "Surely you recall? Or has almost two years in the giddy heights of the exalted Sixth Form dulled your memory in respect of such matters? If you cast your mind back down the misty corridors of time, you will recollect that the primary purpose of the implement that you are holding is to impart an extremely unpleasant sting in the nether regions of girls who displease me! Surely you must remember?"

Set in 1967, Nicola and Angela have now reached the dizzy heights of the Upper Sixth and it is their very last week in school. As usual, at the end of each school year, the Headmistress has urged the girls to raise as much money as they could for the local Children's Home.

Nicola was determined to become a 'legend' in the history of the School and refused to bake cakes or go for a silly sponsored swim to raise money like the rest of the girls. Angela was only joking when she suggested that they should steal Mrs. Vincent's cane and sell it back to her for charity, but Nicola thought it was a brilliant idea!

She decided that with the exception of Crusty Cartwright's, they should steal all of the mistresses' canes and Miss MacTaggart's belt, but would need a good, convincing story to avoid being swished for their audacity. It was Angela who unwittingly supplied the solution. She was still joking when she remarked that canes were not the usual booty of cat-burglars, but Nicola decided that *they* should get the blame!

Will the intrepid girls survive unscathed from their daring exploits?

£15.00

THE SONG OF THE CANE

THE RATTAN CANE is the most painful of all instruments of punishment. It stings, leaves marks and evokes noisy responses; and nobody who has ever been disciplined by one will ever forget the experience. From quite another point of view, a cane is light, long-lasting, and a sensuous delight to use. Its accuracy is phenomenal: it is astonishingly economical of effort; and makes a music like no other implement. *The Song of the Cane* is an anthology of writing—fiction, poetry and factual accounts—carefully selected to provide the broadest possible view of this most dreaded of all implements of correction. Edited by Jacqueline Ophir.

£15.00

THE WHIP AND THE ROD

NOT A BOOK for the squeamish or faint-hearted! *The Whip and the Rod* was written in 1941 to draw attention to the fact that although the *Report of the Departmental Committee on Corporal Punishment* of 1937 had recommended that the flogging of males, and the birching of boys as young as eight, should be discontinued as a permissible judicial punishment in the United Kingdom, the Government of the day had refused to act upon their suggestions. At that time, very few civilised countries in the world still used corporal punishment as a sanction in their penal codes. The punishment was usually used for those who had committed violent offences, especially against women.

£15.00

OUCH!!
A Literary History of the Smacked Bottom

COMPRISING over 150 quoted passages from 500 years of disciplinary writing! The extracts are of all lengths, from single paragraphs to several pages, and of all types. Every possible disciplinary configuration is represented with no overall gender preference. Many passages are moving, others humourous, a few are shocking, and a great many are exciting! The book is laid out with five chapters, each corresponding to a particular era in history. In the first half, the birch rod enjoys almost universal employment, but by the dawn of the twentieth century it is fast falling into eclipse and being replaced by the cane and strap. Although containing some passages that CP fans will be familiar with, the book also features items which have been translated from both French and German literature for the very first time and specifically for use in this book.

£25.00

EXPERIENCES OF FLAGELLATION
A Series of Remarkable Instances of Whipping Inflicted on Both Sexes, With Curious Anecdotes of Ladies Fond of Administering Birch Discipline.

COMPILED by An Amateur Flagellant, this title was first printed and published in London for private circulation in 1885. It quotes many extracts from *The Englishwoman's Domestic Magazine*, relating to the pros and cons of flogging girls. Other anecdotes include: 'Revelations of Boarding School Practices'; 'The Whipping Widow'; 'Lady Preparing for Birching'; 'Flogging and Cruelty in a Glasgow Industrial School'; 'Miss Birched for Thieving'; the notorious case of 'Elizabeth Brownrigg', who was executed for her excesses; and 'Flogging with a Frying Pan'!

£20.00

THE ART OF DISCIPLINE
A Pictorial History of the Smacked Bottom

NEARLY 600 exquisite images from the golden age of disciplinary illustration—including more than 60 from Louis Malteste, over 40 from G. Topfer and more than 30 from Jim Black—plus dozens of drawings by Beloti, Dagy, Hegener, Herric, Milewski, Soulier, Wigead, and many other artists.

Entire classic collections such as 'Three Painful Years', 'Frenzies', 'Flora en Pension', 'A Dominant Mistress', 'Récits Piquants', &c. Hundreds of unattributed drawings covering subjects such as School, Domestic Discipline, Postures, The Weaker Sex, Judicial Punishments, and many others.

There has never been a picture book like it!

£40.00

THE ART OF DISCIPLINE
Volume Two

AT THE TIME it was produced, *The Art of Discipline* was, without a doubt, the greatest single source of disciplinary art ever published between hard covers.

The original volume could not, and did not, claim to be totally comprehensive in its assembly of images and now, this second volume clearly surpasses its highly distinguished predecessor! Comprising 40 per cent more images—820 instead of 570, *The Art of Discipline Volume Two* also contains 16 full colour plates.

Divided into three parts, 'Artists and Collections' depicts the work of the most talented artists through the ages, including many still active today. 'Personalities' is sub-divided into sections featuring 'The Dominant Female'; 'The Dominant Male'; 'The Schoolmaster'; and 'Judicial Punishment'. 'A Miscellany' includes disciplinary scenarios in commercial advertisements, seaside postcards, "what-the-butler-saw" stereo viewing machines, films and TV, comics and cartoons, plus vintage photographs and a selection of spanking machines!

The most comprehensive collection ever assembled!

£50.00

FOR A FULL CATALOGUE OF AKS BOOKS WRITE TO:

PO Box 39, Bexhill-on-Sea, East Sussex, TN40 1WR

Telephone & Fax: 44 (0) 1424 733819

Website: www.aks-books.co.uk

AKS
BOOKS
LIMITED